TRANQUIL SITTING

Yin Shih Tzu

TRANQUIL SITTING

Translated by Shi Fu Hwang
and Cheney Crow, Ph.D

Dragon Door Publications
St. Paul

Published by
Dragon Door Publications
Box 4381
St. Paul, Minnesota 55104 U.S.A.
(612) 645 0517 Fax: (612) 644 5676

First edition, January, 1995
Library of Congress Catalog Card Number:
ISBN: 0-938045-12-1
Cover and interior design by Lightbourne Images
Cover photograph by Tony Aruzza
Printed in the United States of America

Meditation develops your innate energies. With practice, you can take charge of your mind and body, preventing disease before it arises. Shouldn't everyone make an effort to learn something like this? Superficially, meditation looks easy, but if you practice without patience, determination, and a long-term sense of devotion you will never realize its benefits. To give readers a guide to meditation, I have therefore summarized my many decades of experience.

Yin Shih
Tzu
October, 1954

TRANQUIL SITTING

My childhood - My adult history -
Studying Eastern Tantra - The changing
sensations of my physical
body - Eight episodes

Learning the secrets of Tibetan Tantric
Opening the Crown of the Head -
About the practice of Tibetan
Mahamudra

Part II

FOREWORD

By Glenn H. Mullin

In 1954, at the age of eighty two, the venerable Chinese master Yin Shih Tzu put to paper a remarkable account of his experiences in the practice of meditation, in which he had combined Taoist and Buddhist techniques in a traditional blend of spiritual exercises for health and enlightenment. Moreover, he complemented his spiritual biography with a section on practical exercises for inducing the experiences of body and mind that he himself had realized.

From its most ancient times China developed and preserved a most unique culture of meditation for health, harmony and self-fulfillment. The early Taoist masters well understood the nature of the human predicament, and responded by setting forth clear guidelines whereby trainees could extract the essence of the human potential. Later, with the importation of Buddhism from India, these two traditions confronted one another in what may be called a most exquisite marriage of spiritual technologies. Master Yin Shih Tzu addresses this marriage not as historical data, but as a living dynamic. He began his training as a Taoist, and later supplemented his practice with elements from the Tendai and Chan schools of Chinese Buddhism. Several decades later he complemented this body of techniques with several methods coming from the esoteric Vajrayana Buddhism of Tibet. He discusses these with disarming intimacy and humility.

From birth Master Yin Shih Tzu was afflicted by chronic health problems, and as a teenager took up the practice of Taoist yoga and meditation solely in order to cure himself. Only after he had witnessed the healing powers of these techniques did he become fascinated with the spiritual implications of the methods he had been utilizing, and thus begin to apply himself to them from within a spiritual perspective. His account of his experiences in these two areas, firstly medical and then spiritual, thus provides the reader with a glimpse of the multidimensional impact of these ancient practices.

His training in classical Chinese medicine and as a professor of physiology enables him to express both his own experiences and his guide to cultivating a practice of these methods in a language easily comprehensible to the modern reader. He lived in a special period, when China was making the transition from an ancient and somewhat insular culture to a modern nation aware of international attitudes and perspectives. Thus he stood on a bridge in Chinese history, and his education on both sides of the bridge provided him with a unique insight. His book is a wonderful contribution to our understanding of the nature of Taoist/Buddhist yoga, meditation and inner science.

Shi Fu Hwang and Cheney Crow have done an excellent job of translating the manuscript from the original Chinese, and we owe a great debt to them for their efforts.

Glenn H. Mullin
Author and lecturer
October, 1994

FOREWORD

By Stuart Alve Olson

B ack in the late 1960's I acquired a copy of Lu K'uan Yu's work, *The Secrets of Chinese Meditation*, where he includes translations from the materials of Yin Shih Tzu. These materials were quite distinct from other Chinese works on meditation, being presented more as journals and documentation rather than as treatises. As the years went by, and as my knowledge of Chinese progressed, I discovered that the works of Yin Shih Tzu were without question the most popular contemporary sources of meditation instruction for the Asian community. Many Chinese meditation books have borrowed from and even included his entire writings.

His work has indeed been very influential in my own practice. For many years I considered translating this same book, but found myself involved with too many other unfinished projects to add it to the list. Therefore I was elated to find that Shi Fu Hwang and Cheney Crow had completed this new translation with such clarity.

Yin Shih Tzu's given name was Chiang Wei-kuo. He claimed to have been a follower of the Dragon Door Sect (*Lung Men Tsung*) of Taoism. The sect was founded by Ch'iu Ch'ang-ch'un during the Sung Dynasty, 1200 AD, and is a subsect of the Complete Reality School (*Ch'uan Chen Tsung*)- both headquartered to this day at the White Cloud Monastery in Beijing. The Dragon Door Sect maintained two ideologies which made it distinct from other traditions. The first is that the physical body must initially be refined and disciplined before spiritual alchemy could be undertaken. The second ideology integrated the best of the "three teachings"—from Taoism the teachings of Lao Tzu, from Buddhism the Ch'an teachings of Bodhidharma, and from Confucianism the Doctrine of the Mean—into their own system and practices. We can definitely see these influences in Yin Shih Tzu's works.

The popularity of Yin Shih Tzu's work stems from the fact that he was a layman, married with children, a job and responsibilities. He proved without doubt that all lay people, not just monks and nuns of the Buddhist and Taoist orders, were privy to the attainments and benefits of meditation. Further, like all of us must, he underwent an arduous search. He examined many different schools of meditation, met with various teachers and most importantly, came to grips with *discipline*—the very first and most difficult aspect for self-cultivators of meditation.

The very heart of his work is "inspirational hope" for all who want to practice meditation, but may feel that their life contradicts or obstructs that practice. This work clearly shows the illusion of that kind of thinking, as it provides a very practical outline and guidance for lay practitioners of meditation. It is for his lucid writings and his accomplishments in meditation that he is considered one of China's most celebrated lay meditation practitioners.

Meditation is the most practical of all methods of self-cultivation. The ability to concentrate and be tranquil benefits every aspect of our daily life. You need not seek to be a Buddha or to soar in the mystical realms of the immortals to undertake and benefit from the practice of meditation. Meditation is at the apex of all holistic healing. In time it will become the mainstay for providing physical and psychological health and well-being in our society. It is my hope that this English publication of Yin Shih Tzu's *Tranquil Sitting* will bring us closer to that end, and prove as beneficial and inspirational to the English reader as does the original text to the Chinese reader.

Stuart Alve Olson (Upasaka Kuo Ao)
October, 1994

TRANSLATOR'S INTRODUCTION

The Taoists consider that their books on cultivation represent their most secret teachings. They say, "The opportunity to approach a book about the Tao arises only with divine guidance." Yin Shih Tzu's book teaches a way to cultivate. By the simple act of opening this book, you are beginning on a path of cultivation.

The Taoists have always sought the secret of immortality, and many of them have written manuscripts attesting to their attainment of the highest levels of cultivation. Several of these documents describe both methods of cultivation and the individual experiences of the practitioners during their progress. These manuscripts have been passed down from generation to generation, and their instructions followed by aspiring Taoists. In the Han dynasty, Wei Pao Yang wrote *Tsan Tung Chi* (Precepts in Accordance with the Tao) and Li Shao Juan wrote *Huang Ting Ching* (The Book of the

Yellow Court). During the Tang dynasty, Lu Tong Pin wrote *Chao Shih Kao* (The Songs of the Trigrams of the I Ching). During the Yuan dynasty, Chang San Feng wrote *Wu Kan Su Hua Tsur* (Poems about Rootless Flowers) and during the Ming dynasty Wu Tsung Shu wrote *Tien Hsien Tsun Li* (*The Theory of Becoming a Diety*). Other Taoists, including Tsung Li Chuan, Wang Tsung Yang, Chang Tz Yang, Chen Li Wang, Pai Yun Tsan, and Liu Hua Yang during the recent Ching dynasty, left similar manuscripts describing their own experiences in Taoist practice.

Unfortunately, these writers used very arcane language, describing their cultivation in the metaphors of the different Chinese traditions, including theories of Yin-Yang and the Five Elements. Because of this, the uninitiated reader can neither understand nor replicate their methods. Compared to these older manuscripts, Yin Shih Tzu's descriptions seem modern and scientific. His training as a professor of physiology and psychology and his intense desire to convey his experience with absolute and convincing accuracy combine to make Yin Shih Tzu's experiences highly accessible to any reader, and therefore an important contribution to understanding both the meaning and the process of this type of cultivation.

In the diary section of the book, Yin Shih Tzu's earliest entries describe his unhealthy childhood and a brush with death which led him to pursue

Taoist methods of cultivation, initially to heal himself. Once he began practicing these methods of cultivation, his health improved, and he became strong. He continued this practice, with few interruptions, and made regular progress. Throughout his life, Yin Shih Tzu patiently and faithfully wrote vivid and detailed descriptions of all the physical sensations which accompanied his practice of Chen Ts'an Chio (All Truth Doctrine), a type of internal alchemy practiced by many renowned teachers, including Tsung Li Chuan, Lu Tong Pin, Wang Chang Yang and Wu Tsung Shu. Yin Shih Tzu's willingness to document his physical experiences in such detail and provide carefully worded instructions for the preparation and practice of Chen Ts'an Chio allows the reader to witness a Taoist's progress through every stage of internal alchemy.

For Yin Shih Tzu, this process began at the lower Tan T'ien, and slowly moved to the middle and the upper Tan T'ien. He describes the cultivation of the Small Heaven Circulation, the Large Heaven Circulation, and the Reverse Heaven Circulation. He shares the experience of cultivating his vital fluids so that they transform into Ch'i, then cultivating the Ch'i so that it transforms into spirit, and finally cultivating the spirit to return to the void, where the void dovetails with the Tao.

Yin Shih Tzu's word "meditation" in the title of the manuscript actually means tranquil sitting. Tranquility or peace, and the maintenance of good health, has been the stated goal of all religions throughout history. Particular to Taoist philosophy is the cyclical notion that tranquility is achieved when an object stops moving and returns to rest, a state of tranquility which in turn creates perpetual motion. In this way, although things return to the state of tranquility, they do not perish; on the contrary, they generate a source of new energy. Lao Tsu says of this, "Who can make turbulent water be tranquil and who can make it gradually clean and pure? Who can transform perpetual motion to stillness and gradually recover all of his energy? Only the Taoist can achieve this." This statement epitomizes the Taoist idea of tranquility.

Taoism has several sects. Each has its own methods of cultivation. We can differentiate four main methods: focusing the mind on one point, visualization, breathing, and guidance.

Focusing the mind on one point

Focusing the mind on one point is also called focusing on the cavity, or focusing on the mysterious gate. There are four types of focus. The first type focuses on physical points on the body. The second type focuses on points in a void in front of the body, and the third type involves focusing on a specific point in front of the body. A fourth type requires focusing on a point just below the nose and visualizing white light at that point.

Yin Shih Tzu used the first type of practice, in which the focus moves from point to point as the practitioner advances. The progressive points of focus are: first, the Lower Tan T'ien, a point two inches below the navel; next, the Middle Tan T'ien, between the navel and the heart; and finally the Upper Tan T'ien, the cavity between the eyebrows, for the most advanced practice.

When the practitioner focuses the mind on the point or cavity in the body, a flow of energy is generated in his body, which, like a current, flows and pounds in his governor and conceptual meridians. In this process, a large quantity of saliva may be produced, and the practitioner may feel a sensation of heat in the Lower Tan T'ien, if that is where he has been focusing. He may also experience a vision of bright light. Having experienced these sensations after extensive practice of meditation on the Lower Tan T'ien, the practitioner may begin focusing on the Middle Tan T'ien. When he concentrates his focus on his extremities, he will eventually have a vision of a radiant brightness in front of him, and every part of his body will have various sensations. After these experiences occur, the practitioner may move on to focus on the Upper Tan T'ien. These sensations and phenomena will vary according to the specific qualities of each individual practitioner's heredity, mental capacity, knowledge, and education. Each time he meditates the practitioner's experience will be somewhat different.

There is one cautionary note to women who would like to use this method of cultivation. Before their practice, women should perform a preparation described in the book of Chiao Yang Chin. The female practitioner is instructed to rub her breasts by crossing her hands three hundred and sixty times, then take twenty-four breaths. During pregnancy, women are advised to discontinue this type of meditation.

Meditation methods vary amongst the different sects. Some sects have procedures with up to thirty-three separate steps, others twenty-four, twelve, and nine steps. Every sect, however, emphasizes the importance of verbal instruction from teacher to student, and every student must take a vow before instruction may begin. A further restriction applies in all sects — that only one student may receive instruction at a time.

Visualization

This method is also called spirit medicine, or spirit traveling. The practitioner must have been initiated into the practice of opening the crown of the head in order to use this method. In this practice, the consciousness guides the soul out through the top of the head to the heavens, where the practitioner may pay homage to the gods. The practitioner can visualize his soul taking on different human and animal forms, and, after much practice, he may use his mental power to observe the forms he takes on. If he chooses a baby, he can see this baby ascend through his crown into three-dimensional space. When a practitioner reaches this point, he has almost reached the highest level of attainment, and his body will become radiant.

Breathing

There are several breathing methods, including Ch'i-Kung, an internal-external exercise, and the practice of yoga. Five types of breathing methods are used. In the first method, nose breathing is used to send the Ch'i to the Tan T'ien. In the second, inhalation through the nose and exhalation through the mouth are used for expulsion of old air and ingestion of new air. In the third method, the mouth alone is used both for inhalation and exhalation, with swallowing of saliva, holding the breath, and emptying the mind to concentrate only on the breath. The fourth method involves using the skin to breathe and to absorb the essence of the void. In the fifth method, the breath is held, with no breathing in or breathing out.

Guidance

Guidance may be classified into two types, internal and external. The method of guidance, Tao Yin, was used by two famous ancient Taoists, Wu Tsung Shiu and Lu Hua Yang, who said they used their minds to guide the energy flow in their meridians, which they called "turning the irrigation machine". The two levels of this internal guidance method are well known as the "Small Heaven Circulation" and the "Large Heaven Circulation". In the school of tantric study, this method of internal guidance is called "cultivating the energy flow in the meridians", or "kindling the fire of the physical body". The external guidances include taking physical postures, mimicking the posture of a bear hug and a crane stretching his leg, learning to practice acupressure, massage, and internal-external martial arts.

In practicing internal guidance, you focus the mind to guide the Ch'i, beginning at Hui Yin, the pubic region. The practitioner must let the Ch'i trace up the Governor Meridian, pass through the Wei Lu (the tailbone acupoint), Chia Chi (the middle of the spine), Yu Chen (the base of the skull) to reach the Ni Huan (the brain). This process is called 'sending the Yang Fire' to the brain. From the Ni Huan, the practitioner guides the Ch'i to descend to the lower Chiu Chiao (the bridge of the raven), reaching the Shih Erh Tzung Lo (the twelve floors — that is, the throat). From here the Ch'i enters the acupoint of Tan Chung (the middle of the chest), then back to remain at the Lower Tan T'ien (two inches below the navel). This process is called "retreating in accordance with the attribute of the Yin". Each completion of this circle is called a "round" of heaven circulation. In practicing this method, some sects also try to return from the Ni Huan directly back to the Governor Meridian, and pass over the Lower and the Middle Tan T'ien, resting at the point between the eyebrows. This process is called "the reverse turning of the irrigation machine", or the "reverse heaven circulation". Among the sects which practice this process, some use this method in combination with the method of breathing, with the focusing on one point method, or with the visualization method.

Another method of internal guidance is called "cultivating three meridians and the seven chakras." In this practice the Ch'i is guided to trace straight up from the bottom of the body to the crown of the head, or in reverse, descending the same path. This method is practiced in combination with the method of breathing, focusing on one point, and visualization.

Utilizing sexual energy is another cultivation method using internal guidance. In this method, practitioners take on unusual sexual postures, in order that energy produced during sexual intercourse may be directed towards enhancement of the cultivation process.

A different method of guidance practiced by some sects is the method of massaging acupoints and exercising the limbs. After the practitioner undergoes a massage of his acupoints and limbs and he focuses his mind on this process of guidance, some unexplained automatic movements occur. These movements usually involve the practitioner hitting himself about the head and upper body, and this energy is directed to further the cultivation process.

All these guidance methods rely on the practitioner using his mind to unite his spirit with his Ch'i, while using his will to guide his Ch'i to circulate through various parts of his body. There are many important areas to guide the Ch'i, particularly the six "gates", the three back gates (the acupoints Wei Lu, the Chia Chi, and the Yu Chen and the three front gates. The three front gates are the points between the eyebrows, Tan Chung (the center of the chest), and the Lower Tan T'ien. After prolonged practice, this guided circulation of the Ch'i will produce one very specific effect: the practitioner will be able to see his inner light. When this occurs, the practitioner has completed his cultivation.

Comments

In our modern society, there are few people willing to devote themselves to these methods. This is true not only in the Western world, but also in China. Practitioners who wish to attain very high levels are undertaking a very difficult task. It is possible for a practitioner not to aspire to attain the highest levels, but to undertake Taoist practices in order to achieve a healthy body and long life. Cultivation of the Ch'i is known to contribute strongly to maintaining good health and preventing disease. In master Chang San Feng's book, *The*

Secret of Tai Ch'i Internal Alchemy, he recommended many times that practitioners who undertake the cultivation of internal alchemy also practice T'ai Chi Ch'uan, where a specific sequence of physical movements is practiced to maintain the circulation and the stability of the Ch'i. Although each can be practiced separately, Tai Ch'i Chuan and meditation are best practiced together.

Shi Fu Hwang
November 1993

ABOUT THE
TRANSLATION

This text is a translation of a book written in Chinese in 1954 by Yin Shih Tzu (1872-1954), an eighty-two year old Taoist whose meditation practice indicates he was a follower of the Dragon Door sect. In his younger years, Yin Shih Tzu had studied physiology and taught at Kuan-Hua University in Shanghai. Believing that many of the ancient documents about meditation practices and experiences were inaccessible to the average reader because of their complex terminology, Yin Shih Tzu tried to communicate his own experiences as clearly and concisely as possible. His wish was to document his unusual meditation experiences in a strictly physiological sense, and to testify to his personal benefit from the healing powers of Taoist meditation.

The original book is divided into two distinct parts. The first is a careful documentation of the theory, physiological aspects, prepatory steps and instruction for the practice of meditation. The second part is a detailed account in diary form of the author's personal experiences with meditation, his own self-healing which he attributes to his Taoist practice, and finally his initiation into the Tibetan tantric practice of opening the crown of the head. In this translation we have reversed the order of the sections and begin with Yin Shih Tzu's personal experiences.The original Chinese text was published in China as part of a collection of writings on meditation, called *Chin Tsu Fa Chi Yo*, The Collection of the Way of Meditation, Hsi Yo Publications, January, 1962.

In translating this book, we have tried to be faithful at all times to the original text. In the few instances where the text was not clear enough in its translated form, square brackets have been used to indicate words or phrases added by the translators to facilitate reading of a specific passage. Within the text, all parentheses are those of the original author, Yin Shih Tzu. Transcription for Chinese characters was done using the Wade-Giles transcription system.

Cheney Crow, Ph.D.
February 1994

A TAOIST JOURNAL

On the Theory, Practice, and Benefits of Meditation

BY YIN SHIH TZU

PREFACE

C hinese traditional medicine is noteworthy for its preventive benefits. I wanted to write a book that would show how Taoist meditation integrates into this system. Many ancient scriptures describe meditation in both preventive and curative terms, but most of them are written in terminology deriving from concepts not easily understood by the lay reader: terms relating to yin and yang, the five elements, K'an and Li, from the I Ching, or Lead and Mercury, from internal alchemy. Also, the theories behind these scriptures contained secrets which could not be shared with all, so they could not be widely disseminated.

Many years ago I wished to write an easily understood book and present it to the world, but, having little time, I postponed this wish until 1914, when I was forty-two years old, and saw a Japanese method, Okada-Torajirô meditation, named after the man who created it. After this time I could no longer remain silent, so I wrote a book called *Yin Shih Tzu's Meditation.* "Meditation" in Chinese means "tranquil sitting", and has been practiced for several centuries. During the Sung dynasty, Confucian scholars used meditation to regulate their conduct. During the Ming dynasty, Yuan Liao Fan wrote a book called *The Secret of Tranquil Sitting* and in it presented a method resembling the precepts of tranquility found in the Zen school of Buddhism. Since the phrase "tranquil sitting" is easily understood and remembered, I have also chosen it to be the title of my book. Human beings have four basic postures: walking, sitting, lying down, and relaxing. Of these four, only the sitting posture can make the whole body calm down and enter into the state of tranquility, so both the Taoists and the Buddhists chose this posture for meditation. Although it is true that the postures of lying down and walking can also be used for meditation, the practitioner will find that using these postures is more difficult than sitting.

My first publication sold many copies. In 1918, when I was forty-six years old, I wrote another book called *The Continuation of Yin Shih Tzu's Meditation,* in which I interpreted my experiences based on the teachings of Tzu Kuan's principles of the Tien Tai sect of Buddhism. These two books sold very fast and have been reprinted several dozen times. Now thirty-six years have elapsed, and I am eighty-two years old. I have accumulated more experience, and witnessed the existence of extraordinary acupoints and the related eight meridians, which I would like to submit as a reference for medical care. This book presents more material than the previous two books on the theory, method, and experience of tranquil sitting.

PART I

CHAPTER ONE

My Experience

My childhood

In my childhood I was a small, weak, and sickly boy. I felt dizzy, sweated at night, and had sores on my genitals. In my sleep I suffered from spermatorrhea. I saw spirits and ghosts, sound filled my ears. All these physical problems occurred. Occasionally, leaving my house I could walk only half a mile before my feet would soften and become so weak that I could go no further. When I was fifteen or sixteen years old, my health problems became more numerous and more severe. I felt like I was in a trance, I suffered from floating fears, and felt my body struck by waves of heat. I still remember the spring when I was seventeen; every afternoon my body overheated, then became cool again by the following morning. This condition continued until the summer.

I became very sick with tuberculosis, and called on doctors to diagnose me. They prescribed different medicines, but these never improved my condition. In my home I had a Chinese medical book, *I Fen Chi Kuei* (General Answers to Medical Questions), which explained that tuberculosis could not be cured by relying on medicine alone. This book recommends that patients be nursed in quiet surroundings, so that they may recover gradually. The book also introduces the art of Taoist meditation, Hsiao Chou Tien (Small Heaven Circulation), and describes in detail how to develop this practice. I followed the instructions and practiced Taoist meditation. What eventually happened to me convinced me of its effectiveness.

I practiced meditation very diligently when I was ill, but when the symptoms disappeared, I stopped practicing. I lacked devotion. Though occasionally I was still ill, my general health was much better than it had been before I began the meditation practice. When I was twenty-two years old, I got married. Thinking my health was quite good, I gave up the practice of meditation. During this time, however, I had sex too frequently, so my old sickness struck me again. I also ate too much, which resulted in severe stomach aches. My esophagus was feverish, and my stomach made noise constantly. Even when I longed for food, if it was presented to me I could not swallow it.

In the spring when I was twenty-seven, my elder brother died of tuberculosis, and I was also infected. At twenty-eight years old, my coughing became relentless, and later I spat blood. This condition lasted three months. My health was becoming worse each day. Finally, I decided to throw away all my medicines, give up sex, live alone in a separate room, leave all worldly worries behind, and practice meditation. I forced myself to meditate four times a day, at midnight, six in the morning, noon, and at six in the evening. Each time I meditated for one or two hours. I continued this practice for three months. Eventually I felt my abdomen gradually become warm. This feeling of heat became stronger and stronger, until it circulated and trembled in my abdomen like boiling water. On the evening of May twenty-ninth, I felt a jerky quiver in my abdomen, then a flood of hot air flushed against the base of my spine, and, following the Chia Chi sympathetic nerve, surged up to the base of my brain. The meridian along this line is called the Tu or Governor meridian, in the traditional Chinese medical dictionary. I felt this sensation six times, before it gradually stopped.

I realized then that only eighty five days had passed since the first day, March fifth, when I had resumed practicing meditation. After this experience, every time I entered into meditation, the heat would follow the same path, reaching the summit, but the quivering never recurred. It seemed that after the quivering experience, I had been switched into another body. Not only were all my old diseases cured, but I could easily walk for more than ten miles without feeling tired.

Since that time I have never discontinued meditation practice. When I was twenty-nine years old, I was hired as a tutor. I simply rearranged my meditation schedule, changing it to twice a day, once in the morning and once in the evening. On the morning of March twenty-eighth of the same year, I felt the heat quivering in my abdomen again. From there it came up my Chia Chi sympathetic nerve, and flushed against the base of my brain. For three days the heat continued. I felt like the bone at the back of my brain had opened, as a tide of heat flowed into the crown of my head. After this experience, this sensation recurred every time I entered into meditation; the heat flowed along the same path, but without quivering.

At midnight on October fifth of that year, I felt the quivering in my abdomen again, and the heat circulating at the crown of my head changed direction, rushing down my face, separating into two parts around my nose and mouth, then reuniting at my throat. This flush of heat continued down along the vagus nerve, through my chest, then flowed into my lower abdomen. In traditional Chinese medical terms, this path is called the Jen or Conception Vessel meridian.

After this experience, every time I entered into meditation, the heat flowed from my Wei-Lu acupoint (at the base of the spine), up along my Chia Chi sympathetic nerve, and ascended to the crown of my head. Then it went back down over my face and chest to my abdomen. The heat repeated the established circuit through the Governor and Conception Vessel meridians. I did not feel the quivering. Since this time, except for a few instances when I took medicine, I have never been ill again. Therefore I believe that my experience has proven that the Taoist art of meditation has a preventive effect against disease.

My adult history

When I was thirty-one years old, I went to Shanghai to study philosophy, physiology, psychology, and public health. Using this knowledge, I tried to analyze the effects associated with my meditation practice, to increase my understanding of them. This type of training led me to prefer using scientific terms and analysis to describe the theory of meditation. As a result, to illustrate this theory, I gradually gave up using the metaphors of Yin and Yang, the Five Elements, Lead, Mercury, and Yi-Ching's terms such as K'an and Li. I published my first meditation book, *Yin Shih Tzu's Meditation*, in 1914, when I was forty-two years old.

The year I was forty-three (1915), I went to Beijing for the second time. There I studied Buddhism, and my fellow students persuaded me to learn Buddhist meditation also. At that time, Master Ti-Hsien was preaching in Beijing, giving sermons on the sutra of *Yuean-Ju Ching*. From him, I learned the method of Tzu-kuan, the secret of cultivating Tien Tai Tsung, one of the branches of Buddhism. Some of my fellow students urged me to write another book about my meditation, so I wrote down my thoughts, based on my understanding of Tung Meng Tzu-kuan (A child's resting mind) and the practice of *Po-Lo-Mi-T'o* (The Diamond Sutra). This led to the completion of my second meditation book, called *The Continuation of Yin Shih Tzu's Meditation*. After this, I concentrated on cultivating the practice of Tzu-kuan.

Studying Eastern Tantra

When I was fifty-four years old, ten or more of my devoted religious friends intended to study the Eighteen Points of Eastern Tantra with Master E Yin Li. At that time, I had not developed sufficient faith in Tantra. My friends urged me insistently to join them, and since I was curious to know more about Tantra, I attended those teachings. I came to find their ceremonies very ornate and tedious. I did not have adequate time to study Tantra, though, because I was teaching at Kuanhua university and my teaching duties were quite extensive. Because of my busy schedule, I was obliged to give up my study of Tantra. I did not, however, discontinue the practice of Tzu-kuan principles.

The changing sensations of my physical body

In the principles of Tung Meng Tzu Kuan, it says that when one enters into deep meditation, some positive sensations will occur. There are eight of these sensations, which are: lightness, warmth, cold, sinking, pulsating force, itching, dryness, and slipperiness. The first four sensations are without motion; the second four involve motion. Also, in my experience, these sensations do not occur simultaneously. Some come earlier, some later.

When I was around twenty-eight years old, I had the sensations of lightness, warmth, and the pulsating force. My first sensation occurred after a lengthy period of meditation. I felt my whole body become very light, light as a feather. The next sensation was heat in my lower abdomen, and then the pulsating force arose, moving up my spinal nerve to my brain. It crossed to the front of my head, and came down over my face, along the vagus nerve, and reached my lower abdomen. This circulating pattern repeated, with the pulsating force apparently touching my Conceptional and Governor meridians. In the records of traditional Chinese medicine, there are Extraordinary Acupoints and eight other meridians which include the Conceptional and Governor meridians. The first of these meridians is called the Tsung or Impersian meridian The second is called the Tai or Belt meridian, and the others, the Yang Chiao, the

Yin Chiao, the Yang Wei, and the Yin Wei meridians.

For the last ten years I had focused in my meditation exclusively on my lower abdomen. I now shifted the focus to the Middle Tan T'ien. Within only a few days, I felt an enormous change occur in my body. It seemed that six meridians were affected: the Yang Chiao, Yin Chiao, Yang Wei, Yin Wei, Tsung, and Tai. I will try to describe the circumstances in detail.

The first episode

Once, after I shifted my focus to the Middle Tan T'ien, I woke up to meditate at midnight. I felt a sudden tremor in my heart and chest, and my mouth filled with saliva. This continued for several evenings. The tremors in my heart became more frequent, and the pulsating force coursed up to the space between my eyebrows, where I intuitively felt that a red light was emitted. The radiance of this light filled the crown of my head, circulating there for a long time. My whole body felt as if an electric field surrounded me, penetrating at the palms of my hands and the bottoms of my feet. It lasted for one minute, then suddenly stopped at my eyebrows.

After that, this happened every evening. It seemed as though there were some device in my Middle Tan T'ien controlling this circulating current. The current moved up from there to the crown of my head, and my crown turned violently as the current spun around. After this violent turning, the current stopped abruptly between my eyebrows. Then my Middle Tan T'ien trembled again. It seemed there was an electric field surrounding the area in my upper body from my left shoulder to my left leg, making a slanting circle, and my bed and my mosquito net were shaken by this quivering. After the violence, the quivering came to a stop.

The quivering occurred again at the base of my brain, and the pulsating force flowed down along my spine and lingered at the bottom of my spine at the Wei Liu Acupoint. Once again, from my right shoulder to my right leg, I felt the presence of an electric field surrounding the upper half of my body with oblique circles. After violent activity, it abruptly stopped. The current had circulated around my right and left legs and made oblique circles which flushed through the paths of four meridians: the Yin Chiao, Yang Chiao, Yin Wei, and Yang Wei. In my experience, the Extraordinary Acupoints and the eight meridians were consistent with the function of the nervous system. This is true, with no exaggeration.

Every time I meditated and focused on the Middle Tan T'ien, I felt a change occur. One evening the pulsating force flowed across my face, from one ear to the other. It seemed as if there was a horizontal line being drawn, and this line waved to the left and to the right several times. Without warning, the pulsating force stopped between my eyebrows. Then it started again, surging downwards from the top of my head to my chin, making a vertical line. It crossed the horizontal line it had previously traced, forming a cross. The current went up and down this line several times, then stopped abruptly once more at the midpoint between my brows. Starting up again at my crown, the pulsating force curved downward to my chest, then descended to my sexual organ, making it rise up. Coursing down from my head in this way, the force made my organ quiver several times. I felt this curved line of force was flushing through a path which began at my Conceptional Meridian and reached the Governor Meridian.

The second episode

One evening my Middle Tan T'ien felt hot, and I felt a surge of the pulsating force. My whole body was bent forward, then backward, to the left, then to the right. I was waved in this same manner several times, each time being pushed forward, backward, left, then right, with no conscious effort on my part. Next, the quivering came up through my hands, moving my hands in a circular motion as fast as a machine. My hands moved in tandem from side to side.

After this, the pulsating force came up through

my feet, making first my left foot bend and my right foot straighten, then my right foot bend and my left foot straighten. I could not consciously control this motion, it was totally beyond my physical or logical control. Immediately afterwards this activity in my legs and arms stopped, and I felt my head and my torso swell up to a size of about ten feet. (According to Buddhist sutra, this is the sign of becoming a Buddha — that one has achieved a giant stature.) All at once my head bent backwards and my chest swelled even more, until I felt it was filled with an extensive void. Once again I was bent forward, my back swelled up, and I felt a similar sensation of being filled with a large, void space. At this point I had normal sensation only in my lower body, as if I had no upper torso, and my body and mind were filled with this state of void. This feeling was quite pleasant.

The third episode

Another evening, I felt the pulsating force move from my Middle Tan T'ien to surround my spine, circulating from left to right, then right to left, equally in both directions. I felt it move under the skin of my back, from left to right, tracing a big circle, dozens of times. This was repeated in the opposite direction, from right to left. Next I felt it circulate in my abdomen, turning from left to right and right to left around my Conceptual meridian. After this, the pulsating force encircled my waist, moving from left to right, forming a big circle, again, dozens of times, as it had in my back. The circle then reversed directions, from right to left, and repeated the same pattern dozens of times. This sequence indicated that my Tai meridian was flushed through.

After this, the pulsating force spiraled downwards in several dozen progressively smaller circles, in a cone shape which followed the path of the Governor meridian from the back of my crown to my Chia Chi acupoint, then down to the Wei Lu. In passing, the pulsating force flushed through my Governor and Conceptional meridians, then ascended from my Wei Lu up my spine to the crown of my head. It then flowed down from the base of my brain to the Chia Chi, and returned to the Wei Lu. This happened dozens of times. Once more, beginning at my lower abdomen, the pulsating force followed the Conceptional meridian, rose up to the crown of my head, flowed down from the base of my brain through the Chia Chi to return again to the Wei Lu. It traced this path dozens of times. In this way the pulsating force completed the circuit which it had begun within me, touching my Conceptional and Governor meridians from the Wei Lu in my back, the Chao Chi, up to my crown, my face, then dropping down to my abdomen.

The next time it started, it moved in the opposite direction. I think that because my meridians were unobstructed, the flow was able to followed a natural path within my body — it could flow from the front or from the back, which proved that my Tsung meridian and the Tai meridian were at that point totally unobstructed.

The fourth episode

Another night, I sensed this pulsating force in my Middle Tan T'ien, and it drew a spiral with a diameter of about two inches on the surface of my skin. This pattern started at the center of my Middle Tan T'ien and extended out to both sides of my body. This pattern went first to the left, then to the right. Each time it started, the pulsating force traced thirty-six spiral patterns. Afterwards, it moved to my abdomen, and made thirty-six spirals in the same pattern on the skin, first to the left, then to the right. Then the force moved upward, to the skin of my chest, repeating the same circular, spiral motion, first to the left, then to the right, thirty-six times. I had the impression that these three events in my lower body, the center of my body, and my upper body, were pre-arranged in a specific order.

Following this, the force ascended to my crown, and, following a line which spiraled down my spine, it reached my Wei Lu, where it stopped. Then it rose, spiraling around my spine again. In this way it reached my crown, then retracted its path up and down my spine twice. The pulsating force then spiraled up from the left side of my lower abdomen, just left of my Tsung meridian, to my crown, where it started down along the same path. Then it spiraled up from the right side of my lower abdomen, just right of my Tsung meridian, reaching my crown. From my crown, it passed down along the same path.

After this sequence, it encircled my Conceptional meridian, at the level of my head. Next, it passed back down to my lower abdomen, circulated once more, and ascended to my crown. Sometimes it moved in a left to right circular motion in my head, stopping at my forehead. First it circled around my left shoulder, next it circled around my right shoulder, an equal number of times in each direction. Suddenly this pulsating force reached between my fingers, and my fingertips shook with no conscious control. This shaking was very rapid, yet like dancing, for it had a clear and obvious pattern. Just as suddenly the pulsating force passed down from my crown and reached my two feet simultaneously. Both feet were straightened out at this time, and the tips of my toes moved in the same rapid, circular, dancelike pattern as the fingers had moved.

The fifth episode

Another night the pulsating force traced a flat spiral pattern on the skin at the center of my back. Beginning at the center, this moving pattern extended to both sides of my body. First the spiral pattern went towards the left, then to the right, as it had before. Also, just as before, the force traced this pattern exactly thirty-six times. Right after this, the pulsating force created this same spiral pattern with thirty-six repetitions on the skin of my flanks. Next, this pattern was drawn on the skin at the top of my shoulder blades, again with thirty-six repetitions of the spiral. The patterns all seemed to have the same structured form. As I mentioned before, I felt the pulsating force move from the Middle Tan T'ien down to my lower abdomen, then up to my chest. Each time the motion was circular, from left to right, then right to left, with only three repetitions of the pattern. This motion began again at the center of my back, moved down to my flanks, then arced up around my shoulders and armpits, swirling to the left and to the right, three times in each direction.

All the repetitions of the pattern were symmetrical. This was my physiological activity — so marvelous, yet quite beyond my powers of imagination! Again, the pulsating force started at my crown, and spread out to my fingertips, and the tips of all my toes. My fingertips and the tips of my toes then seemed to start dancing again, as they moved in patterns with each of my feet and fingers were alternately straight, then bent. In rhythm with this straightening and bending of my feet and fingertips, my cheeks rubbed up and down against my shoulders. These movements were quite rapid.

Suddenly the pulsating force reached up to my

nose and made my nostrils expand and contract. Next it reached my eyes and made my eyelids open and close in a quivering motion, while my eyeballs rotated in a circular motion. After this, the pulsating force touched the edges of my ears, and my ears moved in a circular pattern that seemed very natural, thirty-six times, from left to right, then right to left.

The sixth episode

Another evening, my Middle Tan T'ien generated the pulsating force, which began with a repetitive circular movement. It started at my two flanks, then it surrounded my waist at the level of the Tai Meridian. The motion of the pulsating force was circular, it encircled me from left to right, then right to left, thirty-six times.

It moved up to my chest, and made a horizontal circle once, then circled first to the left, then to the right, thirty-six times. Next it dropped down to the lower area of my abdomen, made a circle around it, then moved to the left and right, making thirty-six circles in each direction. This circular motion shifted from the lower to the middle to the upper area of my torso and was repeated three times. Then it traced circles vertically up and down the left side of my chest. Next, it repeated this pattern on the right side of my chest. After this, the circles alternated from left to right, consecutively, several times.

The pulsating force changed location again, touching my hands and feet simultaneously. The feeling of the force caused my hands to open, and both my arms spontaneously made rapid circles through the air, from front to back. Next, the feeling touched my feet, making them bend, then straighten. This movement was beyond my conscious control. Occasionally my feet moved close to each other, and the toes touched, with my heels apart. Following this, my two heels touched, and my feet turned out, pointing away from each other. My knees also alternately touched each other, then separated. Suddenly my knees were raised up, and my hips were suspended in the air, waving from left to right. At the same time, my hands and feet moved three times. Then the pulsating force moved up to my cheeks, my lips, my nose, my eyes and my ears, just as I have described it previously, but this time it happened faster.

The seventh episode

One evening, I started to feel the circulation in my Middle Tan T'ien, left and right, as the pulsating force traced a design which extended from my chest to my lower abdomen. Like the ones I described earlier, this pattern was also a spiral, but this time it happened more times, at the middle, lower and upper parts of my torso. At each location, there were sixty repetitions of the pattern instead of the thirty-six I had previously experienced. Suddenly I felt that the spiral drawn on my

Middle Tan T'ien was expanding. I felt hollow inside. From my chest to my abdomen, this spiraling motion was expanding, and I felt completely hollow. Separately at each of the three levels, upper, middle and lower, the circles enlarged, approximately six times. Each time a circle was completed, the feeling lasted about five to six minutes.

After that, the pulsating force went up from my Middle Tan T'ien to my crown, and circulated there. Then it dropped down to my left buttock and my left upper body, and traced an oblong shape around my torso thirty-six times. Once more it ascended to my head, then dropped down again to my right buttock, and right half of my torso, repeating the same oblong pattern, moving up and down thirty-six times. After this, it ascended to my head again, and from the base of my brain it flowed down my spine to my Wei Lu. From there it continued down, and paused in my left leg. It next encircled my left leg, then switched to my right leg, and encircled it, too. It circled each leg thirty-six times.

The eighth episode

One evening, I felt the pulsating force move in my Middle Tan T'ien, my lower abdomen, and my chest. I felt this force move up to my brain, where within my skull I felt the circling movement of the force, right to left and left to right, thirty times.

From the base of my brain it flowed down along my spine to my Wei Lu. At this moment my two feet bent, then straightened, touched each other, then separated. The force next raised up to my abdomen, then up to my two shoulders and to my hands. It ascended to my crown once more, and from there it passed through my cheeks, down my face to my throat. It affected my left shoulder, then my right shoulder, causing them to move in a circular motion — afterwards the same thing happened to my two hands.

Next it reached my feet, which bent, then straightened, then touched each other, then separated. Suddenly, my body was bent into a triangular shape: the pulsating force pushed me onto the floor, so I was lying on my back, supported by my shoulders and my shins, with my torso suspended.

My hips turned left and right, then my flanks turned, making my whole body move at an angle from left to right, slanting. Next, I lay flat on the ground, with the soles of my feet naturally rubbing against each other, then the sole of my left foot rubbed my right leg and the bottom of my right foot rubbed my left — they both rubbed the same number of times.

The pulsating force moved next up to my shoulders and the palms of my hands rubbed each other lengthwise. Suddenly the pulsating force made my two hands rub my neck, then my cheeks, from my chin to my ears, front to back. I continued to rub these places, then the base of my skull, my eyes, the sides of my nose, my ears, then my arms crossed and I rubbed my two shoulders and my upper arms, my left arm with my right hand, and right arm with my left hand.

Next my two crossed hands rubbed my lower abdomen, my chest, then my shoulders, and my back, first the upper back, then the flanks, the hips, the legs, the tops of my feet, my toes, and my arches. Once again this pulsating force raised up. It bent my two arms, then my hands turned to fists, and I patted my shoulders with my fists. The backs of my hands then patted the sides of my neck, under my chin, and my face, in a circular motion around my eyes and on both sides of my nose, then, also in a circular pattern, around my ears. Next my fists patted my temples, and my two hands crossed to my two shoulders, slowly squeezing them, as if kneading them, and again I drew my hands down and squeezed my upper arms. I squeezed my neck and the skin on my face, pinching it between my fingers. I rubbed my chest, my abdomen, my flanks, my lower back, my hips, my legs, the tops of my feet and my arches.

I consider this natural massage a physiological phenomenon. The patting and squeezing was orderly and always balanced in number, it seemed well organized. I think I could never consciously guide myself through this sequence — it was just marvelous!

After this, parts of the sequence I have just described happened every evening. Sometimes one part of the sequence would repeat for more than ten days, sometimes several parts of the sequence would occur in a single evening. This continued for half a year before it gradually diminished, then stopped, and did not recur. After those six months, I did not feel the pulsating force again in the Middle Tan T'ien. This is probably because there was no obstruction in any of my meridians, so I no longer felt any kind of pulsating force.

Here is a summary and classification of all these movement types. There were four kinds: hands waving and feet dancing, tapping, rubbing, and squeezing.

CHAPTER TWO

**My Study and Practice of
Tibetan Mahamudra**

**Learning the secrets of Tibetan
Tantra: opening the crown of
the head**

This Tibetan Tantric secret — allowing you
to be reborn into the Buddha's Pure Land
— has never been taught in the Han nation
of China. This doctrine teaches that on his
deathbed a man can visualize his rebirth in the
Pure Land, allowing his consciousness to leave his
body through the crown of his head. With this goal
in mind, the aspirant learns to recite a secret
mantra. Once the aspirant receives the experience
of opening his crown, and practices this process
frequently, he will be able to follow a defined path
at the time of his death. In 1933 I was sixty-one
years old. I learned this secret from Master No Na.
At the time he showed me the secret, he wanted

me to practice at home. Despite my practice, however, I didn't experience the desired effects.

In the spring of 1937, when I was sixty-five years old, I heard that Master Sheng Lu was teaching this secret in Nanking. Four sessions had already been taught. It was said that every participant could open his crown during the session. When the fifth session was about to start, I thought I shouldn't miss this opportunity, so I hurried to Nanking. I reached P'i Lo temple in Nanking that same day, and enrolled in the class for opening the crown (which is called Po Wa — breaking the roof tile).

On April 1, I arrived at P'i Lo temple, and received the empowerment called pouring the blessing through the opening of the crown. This ceremony was much more complicated than Master No Na's. The Master taught us to recite the Ho Mu Chin Kang mantra to facilitate the process. Although the mantra was not long, the method of visualization was quite tedious and complicated, and we had to recite the mantra a hundred thousand times. However, we didn't have much time and the requested number of repetitions was impossible to complete in the space of only a few days, so all of us recited the mantra as many times as possible before receiving the empowerment.

Beginning on the second day, I stayed in my lodgings, shut the door and didn't go out. I concentrated on reciting this mantra until the morning of the last day, by which time I had recited the mantra sixty-two thousand times. In the afternoon of this same day, I changed my lodging to the P'i Lo temple. There were thirty-nine other participants in this training. It was said that this session had more participants than the previous sessions. The Master had us shave a small circular area of hair at our crowns, so that he could examine it during the process of opening the crowns. Accordingly, he prepared some lucky reeds, which were to be inserted in the opening which would occur in the shaved, circular area of our crowns.

On the tenth day the temple gate was closed. An ornate altar was set up in the temple's imposing hall. The hall was exquisitely decorated. The Master called us before the altar to receive the empowerment. Every day there were four classes, each of which lasted for two hours: the first class lasted from seven to nine in the morning, the second class, from ten to twelve, the third, from three to five in the afternoon, and the fourth, from seven to nine in the evening. The empowerment procedure involved visualizing the Patron Buddha sitting at the top of one's head. From my crown to my pelvis, there was a vessel meridian which was blue colored on the outside and red on the inside, and my Lower Tan T'ien had a shining pearl which rose from there to my heart. Then I shouted "Hey", with effort, and visualized this pearl rising rapidly with this sound, dashing out through my crown to the heart of the Patron Buddha. Then again I called out, not quite so loud, "Gha" and visualized the pearl returning through my crown from the heart of the Buddha, and dropping back down to its place of origin in my Lower Tan T'ien. Every session everyone shouted so loudly that they became hoarse and perspired so heavily that their clothes were wet all the way through. (At this time it was still cold, and everybody was wearing thin cotton jackets.) The Master saw that most of us were tired, so he sang a Sanskrit song and wanted us to sing in unison with him so that we could be refreshed by singing. During these two hours, we had four or five rest periods.

Owing to my meditation practice I had an unobstructed central channel running from my pubic region to my crown, and I was able to feel wonderful effects on the eleventh day. In the first class, my crown emitted red light, and my size increased to a great stature. In the fourth class, I felt as if there was a force drilling against my crown, and the pearl was dashing up constantly. When I lay down I felt that my head was emitting white light.

On the twelfth day, I practiced as I had the previous day, and in the second class I felt my skull was splitting at my crown. The two bones covering this spot were separating. In the third class, my head swelled up and a lump appeared at my crown. It seemed as though my scalp would split.

In the first class on the thirteenth day, I felt that every layer of my brain had been pierced. At first,

I felt that my skull was quite thick, then the drilling made it become thin. In the third class, I suddenly felt my upper body to be in a void state, and my head emitted light. The light's luminosity was increasing. In the first and second classes of the fourteenth day, the pearl was shooting up to the feet of the Patron Buddha, and I felt this route was smooth and unobstructed. The splitting felt quite different in nature from the previous day. Because of the change in sensation on the previous day, I thought that the route was still in some way obstructed. In the first class, I felt my neck was a freely flowing column which led directly to my stomach and my intestines. Prior to this, I had thought that my central channel was opened and unobstructed, which was only my imagination, since it was now proven to be true.

In the first class of the fifteenth day, I felt there was a cavity at my crown. In the second class, the Master ordered us to move closer to the window, where the sunshine was brighter. Next he called each one of us to come up so that he could perform the ritual that would make the crowns open, and then insert a lucky reed into this opening as a token of remembrance. If a practitioner's crown was actually opened, the grass would be sucked in and the scalp would seal up around it. I was among those who had reached this level of attainment. The first time there were twenty eight persons whose crowns were opened. For the other eleven persons the grass could not be inserted, which indicated they needed to receive more instruction. All of us whose crown had been opened would not continue the practice of this ritual. However, we came up to the altar and used the power of visualization to help those who hadn't had their crowns opened, to help facilitate their attainment in the procedure of opening the crown.

On the sixteenth day, all of us who had their crowns opened again came up to the altar to help. In the first class, another nine persons' crowns were opened. The last group included a nun and a Buddhist woman who could not have their crowns opened. This nun had practiced secret Tantric arts in Japan. Her attainment was quite profound, yet she had great difficulty in making her crown open. A person shouldn't be overconfident, and should always receive teachings with humility. Otherwise, your goal can be difficult to attain. As for this Buddhist woman, I thought she was old and lacked intelligence. The Master called those in the last group to come in front of his cushion, and then personally empowered them. About an hour later, with the assistance of all of us who had their crowns opened, she had her crown opened.

Afterwards I primarily practiced meditation using the principle of Tzu Kuan, and I practiced Po Wa (opening the crown). On the 24th of May I entered into meditation and felt quiet surround me. My chest emitted light which gradually increased and surrounded my whole body, until the light became a large circle. Previously, I had felt light emit from my head, but this was the first time

I had felt light emit from my chest region. However, I was still conscious of my existence and my whole body was not totally transparent.

On the twenty-sixth day, when I entered into meditation and became quiet, I felt my back emit light, and my whole body was surrounded by brightness, which gave me a very pleasant feeling, but I still felt I had a body which was not in a void state.

On the twenty-seventh day, when I entered into meditation and became quiet, I emitted very bright light which shot up into the clouds and my soul parted from me. Later I gradually drew it back through my crown.

On the 31st day of the same month, after I entered into meditation, my upper body emitted light just as it had the day before. I felt my lower abdomen was boiling like water. My lower body was in a void state, also emitting light, which had never occurred before.

On the tenth of June, after I entered into meditation my whole body emitted a very bright light and I felt as if I had no head. There appeared only a transparent light.

On the fourteenth of June, after I entered into meditation my whole body emitted light. Both my upper and lower body were shining with a transparent light.

On the seventeenth day of June, after I entered into meditation, my whole body emitted light, and I felt it illuminate my mind and eyes. This was so bright that my entire body, top, bottom and sides, was surrounded with a light which expanded into a large circular shape.

On the eighteenth day, after I entered into meditation, my whole body emitted light, and this light was even brighter. My entire body was surrounded with bright transparent light. The light seemed like a single guided burst, directed to the four corners. My consciousness was travelling through the air. Then I withdrew it and returned to my lower abdomen, and as I continued with this practice, my consciousness went down to my feet, up to my two hands and back to my head.

About the practice of Tibetan Mahamudra

In 1947, when I was seventy-five years old, I followed Master Gonga to learn Mahamudra. In the exoteric school of Sutrayana, the most popular sects are Pure Land and Zen. The Pure Land sect claims that your karma follows you into rebirth. The Zen sect emphasizes the process of training the mind to be tranquil in order to attain wisdom, to eventually attain Buddhahood. Tibetan Tantra's secret of opening the crown demonstrates a way to rebirth in the Pure Land and Mahamudra itself has the Zen school's characteristic of tranquility. However, I found the methods of Mahamudra practice more practical and workable than those of Zen and Pure Lands, so from that time on I have continued the Mahamudra practice. Maybe someone would ask me, "I know that you have studied Buddhism, first you study the Sutrayana, and then you study the Vajrayana - this is quite contrary to the proper attitude towards acquiring knowledge, don't you think your knowledge is too impure? How can you actually achieve your goal?" I would answer, "It is not so. Though I have studied different schools, I have never abandoned the practice of striving for tranquility, and all these schools are just helping me to make progress towards attaining tranquility."

When you learn the secret of Po Wa (breaking the crown), you can have the promise of rebirth. When you learn Mahamudra, your practice of tranquil abiding can grow from a shallow state to a profound state. When people thought I was confused in my knowledge, actually my learning followed a straight line, and perseveres.

These two methods, Mahamudra and the Po Wa, which form the experience I have cultivated and practiced, are very popular in the province of Sekong and in Tibet. They do, however, require personal instruction by a lama.

This practice should not be undertaken alone. Readers, please pay attention to this warning.

PART II

Yin Shih Tzu sitting in meditation

CHAPTER THREE

The Theory of Tranquil Sitting

The meaning of tranquility

Our earth rotates continuously. Compared with the size of the earth, human beings seem almost ant-like, yet we cannot sense the earth's movement at all. We are ceaselessly active. Even when we sleep, our heart beat never stops. Our universe is full of constant activity, without a moment's stillness. For this reason, I say that the terms stillness and activity exist only as relative concepts. When the activity of our bodies and our minds is out of sync with the rhythm of the earth's activity, we call both "action." When we don't act and our state synchronizes with the rhythm of the earth's activity, we call this stillness.

After a person has worked for some time, he has to rest. After working for several hours, a factory worker must have time to rest. In schools, teachers strain their brains during a fifty minute class and have ten minutes afterwards to rest. This rest is a state of stillness. However, this state of stillness may not be complete physically and mentally. Sometimes the body is resting, but the mind remains active, and we cannot sense the true meaning of stillness.

The conflicting states of the body and mind

The mind and body are always in conflict. Until we become aware of this conflict, we cannot sense it. For example, if a person behaves badly, he will face a struggle with his conscience, whether he is good or ill-natured. Prompted by his desires, a person behaves badly and later regrets his behavior. This is the conflict between the mind and the body. The ancients called this "the struggle between conscience and desire". A man who can use his conscience to subdue his desire is called a good man. When his conscience overpowers his desire, this conflict is resolved.

Why is there so much conflict? Because no element in the universe exists without another, conflicting element, which is its complement. When each element is confronted with its complement, the two become opposites. The directions are East, West, South and North. The sizes are small and large, high and low, long and short. Shapes are round and square. Time is ancient or modern, going or coming, morning or evening, winter or summer. Men's affairs bring happiness or calamity, joy or anger, love or hatred, righteousness or sinfulness, kindness or evil. Witnessing these polarities, we know that each of our activities will eventually produce its opposite. Activity brings contradiction into being. A man who has a high level of cultivation has a placid and quiet mind. He does not allow the self to exist, and thus achieves selflessness. When he meets with conflicting situations, he can rely on his consciousness to guide him and so reconcile the conflict. Tranquil sitting is the practice that allows this process to be effective.

CHAPTER FOUR

The Physiological Features of Meditation

The relationship between tranquil sitting and normal physical function

Tranquil sitting can influence the entire physical body, including the arms and legs externally and the organs internally. No part of the body remains unaffected by meditation. I do not, however, intend to give a discourse on physiology, so I won't give detailed illustrations of these effects. I will just try to give a general description of the nervous, circulatory, respiratory and regenerative systems.

In the past, people preferred to regard mind and body as two separate entities. Recently, though, the physiologist Pavlov discovered that the cerebral cortex dominates both the external and internal aspects of the body's equilibrium, and generates all of its reflexes. We can therefore affirm now that the human spirit and physical body are not two different things and cannot be separated - they are a unified system.

There are both conditioned and non-conditioned reflexes. Non-conditioned reflexes are innate, instinctive rather than learned behavior, and are the simpler type of reflex. For example, the eyes close abruptly upon contact with an object. The nose sniffs in reaction to the stimulus of a smell. The throat coughs or vomits upon contact with an unpleasant stimulus. The hands withdraw abruptly upon contact with a hot object. All these are non-conditioned reflexes.

There are never enough such reflexes to deal with the changing environment of daily life. However, when similar non-conditioned reflexes accumulate sufficiently, the cerebral cortex is able to link them and transform these into a conditioned reflex. For example, the plum has a sour flavor; eat a plum, and the mouth waters. This is a non-conditioned reflex. Later, you can see a plum and, without putting it into your mouth, produce saliva, quenching your thirst. What was previously unconditioned has become conditioned. Through such associative reactions, [and the transformation which may ensue] people can free themselves from the restrictions of unconditioned reactions [by consciously transforming them into conditioned reflexes].

Just as our thoughts may be replicated in written and verbal language, a second type of stimulus signal can be generated by our thoughts, to replicate the first type of signals, those produced by real physical stimulation. By practicing this method, the limits of the conditioned reflex are eliminated. Physical reflexes have two features: excitation and suppression. When a nerve is stimulated, the entire body, as well as the site of the stimulus, will be excited by the brain. When the excitation reaches a certain threshold, this reaction will be suppressed by the brain.

What has tranquil sitting to do with the nervous system? When the brain simply reacts to stimuli, this state may be called, in religious terms, random thinking. When random thinking arises, or diminishes, there is not a moment's stability. This can disturb the mind, making it uneasy, and furthermore it can influence the health of the physical body.

When someone is caught in the middle of a secretive act, he will blush. If a person meets with a sudden shock, his face will appear greenish white. This indicates that emotional reactions influence the activity of the blood vessels. When you feel ashamed, your arteries expand; if you feel shock or a sudden surprise, your veins expand. If you feel happy, you will have a good appetite. If you feel sad, you can look at food, but cannot bring yourself to eat it. This indicates that emotional reactions can also influence the function of the stomach and the digestive system.

There are many such illustrations, which indicate that our spirit should be calmed down, so that the function of our reflexes will return to normal. The autonomic nervous system, which includes the sympathetic nervous system and the subsympathetic nervous system can maintain balance, so that our bodies and minds may remain in harmony. However, random thinking is difficult to control. A practitioner could devote himself to meditation and continue practicing for a long time before his entire body could be unified, and he would be able to control all parts of his body. The ancients say that when you can sit tranquilly your power over the body is like that of a king surrounded by a hundred subjects who await your command. So we can see the close relationship between meditation and the central nervous system.

The circulatory system

Blood is an element fundamental to human life, for it circulates throughout the body without a moment's pause. The circulatory system includes two main parts, the heart and the blood vessels. The heart is the central device, pumping out red blood through the arteries to the whole body as it simultaneously receives the veins' purple blood. Blood vessels are channels for transferring blood to all parts of the body. One type of channel is called an artery. The vein, another type of channel, returns blood to the heart. The task of the circulatory system is to maintain the blood's balance in the body so that the activity of each part of the body can meet the requirements of the whole body and develop. In this process, each of the circulatory system's tasks may be modified relative to the activity of the whole body. When a specific part of the body is especially active, blood circulation in this area will intensify, so more blood accumulates. For example, when you are full of food, the blood in the stomach will circulate more intensely. After exercising, the limbs will feel full because of the rapidly circulating blood. The opposite is also true; inactive limbs will feel the shortage of circulation. Thus, at all times, every part of a healthy body will receive an appropriate amount of blood, neither too much nor too little. The circulatory system can function normally.

The circulation of the blood and the body's continuous functioning do not depend solely on the expansion and contraction of the heart and blood vessels. The functions also rely on a generalized organization which regulates the entire system. It is the central nervous system which governs these activities, primarily the cerebral cortex. Pavlov said that the nerves of the blood vessels which connect the brain and spine to the heart have two functions: excitation and suppression.

The first of these, excitation, will quicken the heart-beat, contracting the diameter of the blood vessels. The latter will weaken and slow down the heart-beat, and make the blood vessels dilate. These two functions are reciprocal, and are intrinsically related, for the adjustment of the activity of the circulatory system.

When the circulatory system is inactive, a person becomes ill. Both Chinese and Western doctors check the pulse for diagnosis. Whenever the circulatory system is sluggish, there must be either an internal or external cause.

The internal causes may be:

(a) Though the internal organs are in the domain of the central nervous system, they still take orders from the spinal nervous system and the autonomic nervous system (sympathetic and sub-sympathetic systems), which connect indirectly with the brain. The onset of a disease causes the internal organs to have an abnormal reflex, and the flow of blood will become unstable.

(b) A person's blood is mostly preserved in an area of the stomach where its muscles are powerless. Sometimes the muscles cannot expel the blood entirely, so the blood becomes stale. This condition leads to insufficient blood in some other part of the body.

(c) Since we cannot directly influence the activity of the internal organs, we cannot sense when the blood becomes sluggish. Even if we are aware of this situation, we can do nothing but wait until the disease occurs, and then consult a doctor.

(d) The arteries' blood begins close to the heart, therefore it is powerful. The veins' blood starts from the region of the head and the four limbs and then returns to the heart. It remains comparatively far from the heart beat, so its power is much weaker, which is why the veins' blood can easily be retained in the abdominal area.

The external causes.:

Obvious effects are the seasonal changes from summer to winter, the flu, and external wounds of physical and chemical origin, all of which make the circulatory system lose functional properties.

When you maintain a practice in which you focus on the abdomen as your center of gravity, your abdominal muscles will, after much practice, become powerful and flexible. You are able to expel stale blood from the abdominal area, and let it return to the heart. You will also feel stronger sensations from the internal organs. If an internal organ functions improperly, you can sense this situation earlier, and through meditation restore the circulatory system to perfect condition. You cannot easily contract an illness. Practicing this preventive medical care is much better than contracting an illness and then consulting a doctor for a cure.

Breathing

Breathing plays an essential role in supporting human life. Everyone realizes the importance of eating to maintain life. If you stop eating, you will suffer hunger and thirst, and eventually die. However, breathing is more important than eating. If a man fasts for seven days he could die, but if his mouth and nose are covered and he doesn't breathe, he cannot survive longer than half an hour. This illustrates that breathing is more important than food. You need to exchange money for food, and acquiring money depends on your wages. As for breathing, you can obtain air freely from the atmosphere, a process which requires neither money nor labor. That is the reason ordinary people realize the importance of food, but do not realize the importance of breathing.

Energy and calories are necessary to human bodily functions, and are derived primarily from the oxygenization of foods. The stomach is like a steam engine. Digestion of food is just like the burning of a steam engine. In terms of physics, this burning requires oxygen and produces carbon dioxide. In the process of oxygenation, oxygen and carbon dioxide, which came from our atmosphere, return to it. This is an exchange of internal and external bodies, as is breathing. When oxygen is inhaled, it reaches the lungs, then the heart. It makes the blood travel from the veins to the arteries, and, transferred through the arteries, the blood travels to other parts of the body. Then it leaves the blood vessels and begins its restorative role in cell production, during which the cells will generate carbon dioxide, a poison which must be expelled from the body. The carbon dioxide then retraces this route in reverse, from the veins to the heart, from the heart to the lungs, and finally to the mouth and nose, where it is exhaled.

The air entering or exiting the lungs depends mainly on the activity of the chest muscles and the diaphragm. This is the activity of breathing, and it functions incessantly day and night, (in actuality, there is an almost imperceptible pause in breathing and in the heartbeat), so that you can keep your inhalation and exhalation in balance. It is governed entirely by the central nervous system.

When we breathe, the air is taken in through the nostrils and throat, to the trachea, the bronchia, and into the lungs. When we breathe out, the air in the alveoles follows the original route to exit. The lungs are divided into left and the right. The left lung has two lobes. The right lung has three lobes. Physiologists estimate that man's lungs have a total of seventy five billion alveoles, which, spread out, would cover an area of about seventy square meters. About fifty-five square meters are involved in the functions of breathing. Relatively speaking, this space is thirty times larger than the surface area of the human body. We cannot imagine that such a small chest could contain so much. This illustrates to us how elaborate the construction of the lung is.

Though breathing may sometimes involve nitrogen and steam, these are not essential substances. Inhaling is primarily ingestion of oxygen. Exhaling is expulsion of carbon dioxide. This process is necessary to make the purple color of blood in the veins change to a red color before it flows into the arteries. Hence the circulation of the blood is totally dependent on the assistance of breathing. In continuous circulation, the blood makes a circuit through the entire body every twenty-four seconds, which results in thirty-six hundred circuits in a twenty-four hour period. The breathing of a human being may reach twenty thousand repetitions in a day, an intake of approximately three hundred eighty cubic meters of fresh air.

If we estimate that the volume of blood in every person's body is 2.5 liters, then 9,000 kilograms of blood are purified daily. It is difficult to believe that people cannot sense this remarkable event.

The combination of one inhalation and one exhalation is called a single breath. People's lives depend on this breath. If you cannot catch your breath in time, you will suffocate and die. The practice of meditation addresses this problem, which is a fundamental requirement of life. All the Buddhist and Taoist priests and health instructors emphasize the practice of breathing. The initial step is to teach breathing techniques, and even when you attain a high level this practice is continued.

Regeneration

Regeneration is a common characteristic of all living things, the signature of life's activity, the demarcation between living and non-living beings. Regeneration is a basic physiological activity of a highly evolved being. The structure of the human body has attained a very high level of complexity. It requires nutrition and oxygen for its regeneration, a process which involves a sequence of very complicated functions.

Waste byproducts from the regenerative process also undergo a very elaborate process before being eliminated from the body. Waste substances produced by the human being are solid, liquid and gas. The solid and liquid wastes can be eliminated as stool, urine, and perspiration. Gas can be expelled through the lungs and the mouth or nose. Among these, the procedure of expelling gas is the most important for good health. Circulation and breathing, whose functions are assured by the central nervous system which regulates all bodily events, are also auxiliary activities of regeneration.

The regenerative process has two parts. One is constructive regeneration, which includes our body's development, replenishment, the restoration of energy, and nutrition. A growing child has not completed his development; his constructive growth is still in progress. An adult has reached his full development, so replenishment is his body's main task. Another type of regeneration involves the process of breaking things down, whether it be of tissue, energy or food. Any such process can produce energy and calories. After the production of energy, part of it can be used to maintain body temperature, and the excess parts are quickly released from the body. In other words, the procedure of regeneration includes two continuous and inseparable steps.

The first of these steps is the compounding and the breaking down of tissue or food. The second step is the production, use, and release of energy. This regenerative procedure will ensure that our body's old cells continuously break down, as new cells are continuously produced. Physiologists estimate that man's cells are in continuous transformation, a transformation which lasts for seven years, after which time his entire body has been changed into another body. We look in the mirror and find that our faces change between childhood and adolescence, then from adolescence to middle age, until old age, when we can see that our face is totally different. This proves that regeneration is continuously changing our body in an undetectable way, yet we cannot sense this happening. How stupid we really are!

Meditation can make our central nervous system calm down, so that it can develop its potential, to let the blood's circulation function better, to let the breathing system receive its adjustments, and to help the regenerative processes. The effective-

ness of meditation practice on these processes is
impressive.

CHAPTER FIVE

How to Meditate

What adjustments to make before and after meditation

Adjusting your diet

The human body is like a machine. A machine requires fuel to operate just as the human body requires food. After being chewed in the mouth, food is blended with saliva, then digested by the liquids in the stomach and turned into a pasty substance which flows into the small intestine for use by the whole body. We know that food plays a very important part in life. However, if too much food is taken in, the stomach cannot fully digest and absorb it; on the contrary, the undigested waste will be expelled from the body. This will increase the stomach's work. Our bodies will be overburdened, and we will become anxious. In this condition we cannot achieve peace in meditation.

If too little food is consumed, we will suffer from malnutrition and physical weakness. This is not appropriate for meditation either. Therefore, we should regulate our food intake. People always like to eat a lot. This is very inappropriate. We should consume food only until we feel somewhat, but not entirely, satiated. There is an old saying that the body should constantly labor, and food should constantly be regulated. This saying I agree with entirely. We should also not require food with a rich flavor. Vegetables are actually more suitable for our body than meat. It is not good to meditate immediately after eating. We should wait about two hours. The most appropriate time for meditation is in the morning after waking, washing one's face, drinking some water, and emptying the bowels.

Adjusting your sleep

After exerting yourself physically and mentally you need to rest in order to renew your energy. We can regard sleep as the longest period we have to really rest. An ordinary person should sleep for eight hours. Exceeding this will make our spirit lose clarity, which is inappropriate for meditation. With too little sleep, our body cannot recover its energy, and our mind stays in a trance-like state. This also is inappropriate for meditation.

Therefore, sleeping should be fixed at a regular time in order to keep our spirit always clear. This creates the best condition for meditation. We can practice meditation sitting on a bed, before going to sleep in the evening, or wake up at midnight to sit in meditation. After meditation, if we feel the need, we can go back to sleep. In any case, time spent sleeping should neither be too much nor too little.

Adjusting your body

Adjusting your body implies adjusting your posture. We should adjust our bodies before, after, and during meditation. Our physical activities include walking, relaxing, sitting, and lying — four postures. The meditation practitioner should be aware of his behavior at all times. His physical behavior should be easy and calm; violent movement is inappropriate. When you behave violently, your energy flow becomes violent, too, and your mind cannot focus on meditation. Therefore, before meditation adjust the mind. This is another method of adjusting the body.

When you enter into meditation on a bed or on a specially made cushion, loosen your belt, and arrange your feet in the right position. If you fold both your feet, put your left foot on the right thigh, level with the thigh, then put the right foot on the left thigh. In this posture, the soles face upward, the thighs seem to form a triangle, the two knees press tightly against the bed or cushion, and all the body's muscles are like a fully stretched bow. This is the best posture for meditation, for the practitioner will not lean forward, backward, left or right. However, older persons might have trouble using this posture. They can use a half-folded (single fold) posture — putting only the left foot on the right thigh, no need to put the right foot on the left thigh. Some persons might even have problems with the single fold posture; these persons may sit simply with the legs crossed, one foot touching the opposite thigh. The two hands should be in the right position — both hands open, facing up, with the right hand in the left palm, near the abdomen, resting gently on the legs. Then twist the torso in both directions, left and right, to be certain the posture is well adjusted and stable. The spinal column should not be too stiffly erect, nor too bent. Keep the head erect, so that the nose and the navel are vertically aligned.

At this point open your mouth and exhale the stale air from the chest, curling your tongue back extending towards the throat, with the under surface of the tongue in contact with the palate. Next, one should inhale clean air gently three to seven times through the nose. Then the mouth should be closed, with the tongue in the retroflex position, eyes closed and posture straight and motionless. If you feel the body leaning in any direction, adjust your body to correct this. This is how to adjust your body during meditation.

After meditation (to be described later), open the mouth and breathe out at least ten more times in order to reduce the body temperature. Slowly twist the torso in both directions, lift, then shrug the shoulders, and rotate the head in a circular motion. Then slowly and gently unfold the crossed feet and legs. After this, rub the inner edges of the hands against each other, at the lower part of the thumbs, until they become warm. Before opening the eyes, use these warm parts of the hand to wipe the two eyelids. The back of the thumbs should be used again to rub the two sides of the nose simultaneously. After this, rub the two palms together until they become warm, then, with the two warm palms, rub the back of the ears and the head, chest and abdomen, arms, legs, and both sides of the feet. During meditation the blood circulates more actively, making the body perspire, so wait until the perspiration dries before beginning your regular schedule. This is how to adjust the body after meditation.

Adjusting the breath

Air enters and exits through the nostrils as inhalation and exhalation. One inhalation with one exhalation counts as a single breath. The most essential task for meditation is to adjust that breath. There are four different breathing techniques. The first of these is to breathe with the throat. Ordinary people do not realize that breathing is part of the art of maintaining good health;

their breathing is short and shallow. They just let air enter and exit from the short portion of their throats. In this kind of breathing, the lobes of the lungs cannot fully expand and contract. Therefore they cannot fully inhale oxygen and exhale carbon dioxide. This prevents the circulation of blood in the lungs from reaching ideal levels.

The second technique is chest breathing. This technique should be better than the first one, since air reaches the chest and the lobes of the lung fill with air. When we exercise, we use this technique naturally. However, neither of these techniques qualify as breathing adjustments.

The third breathing technique uses the abdomen. This technique allows you to send the breath all the way to the abdomen. When the practitioner uses this technique to inhale, the air is drawn into and fills his lungs. His lungs are expanded and the diaphragm presses down. At this point, the chest is empty and relaxed, and the stomach expands. When the practitioner exhales, the abdomen contracts and the diaphragm raises up against the lungs, so that the stale air in the lungs is fully expelled from the body. This method may be considered a breathing adjustment. Breathing should not take too much effort. Make the breathing slow and prolonged, both as it enters and exits the body. The air should reach the abdomen in a very natural way, noiselessly, so that you cannot hear the breath as it enters or exits the body. This can be considered an advanced breathing adjustment.

The fourth method is to breathe with the whole body. After several years of meditation, the practitioner achieves breathing which he cannot perceive in any way. Reaching this high level of skill, the practitioner appears to others to be in a state of non-breathing, because the rhythm and the volume of his breathing are so reduced. Though advanced practitioners obviously still have their lungs, they seem to ignore their use. Air seems to go in and out though the pores of their skin. A person who can attain such a level has reached the highest extreme of attainment in breathing adjustment.

Pay careful attention to the breath going in and out through the nostrils. Do not inhale sharply, for this is shallow breathing. Learn to extend the breath from the throat to the chest and to the abdomen. This is the breathing adjustment to use before meditation. During meditation, if the breath is not adjusted, your mind will be unstable. Therefore, adjust the breath to a slow and gentle pace, balancing the duration of the inhalations and exhalations to make them equal. Regulate the breath by counting, either counting the number of exhalations or the number of inhalations. Count first from one to ten, and repeat this count. If your concentration fails during the first ten breaths counted, then start again at one. Continue this practice for quite some time, for it helps develop your skills, and adjusts the breathing correctly. This is part of the method for breathing adjustment during meditation. Breathing adjustment influences the circulatory system, making the blood flow more actively and warming the body. Therefore, after meditation, open the mouth and release the breath to lower the body temperature and re-establish normal body temperature. At this point, you may resume your activities. This applies to the method for breathing adjustment after meditation.

Adjusting the mind

Right from birth, people seem to enjoy the mind's random thinking. As each random thought dies another arises to take its place. We can describe it this way: "Just as the will gallops like a horse, so the mind acts like a monkey" We can see that the mind is very difficult to adjust. The final result of meditation depends totally on how well you adjust random thoughts. Of the four postures, sitting, lying, walking and relaxing, we should occasionally check our walking and relaxing. All verbal and physical behavior should be monitored. We should always put our mind inside our bodies; do not let it gallop at random. With prolonged training, it will be easier to adjust the mind. This is how to adjust the mind before meditation.

During meditation, there are two types of problem. The first is that the mind may lose concentration, and not be able to complete the meditation process. The second is that the mind becomes drowsy, and easily drifts towards sleep. The beginning practitioner may easily encounter the problem of losing concentration. After a long period of practice, he will be able to diminish the frequency of random thoughts. Then he risks the problem of getting drowsy. These two are the most frequent problems faced in meditation.

The way to cure the problem of losing concentration is to relinquish all anxieties and look at the physical body as something external to yourself, without thinking about your existence. Focus your mind on the lower abdomen, and gradually you can experience profound tranquility. The way to cure the problem of drowsiness is to focus your mind on the tip of the nose. Then you can raise your spirit. In my experience, it is easy to become drowsy during evening meditation after working hard during the day. In morning meditation you would not have this problem.

I am recommending some techniques to choose from. The first of these is accurately counting from one to ten. After extensive practice, your mind will follow the breath. With this technique alone, the two problems of losing concentration and of drowsiness may be cured. This is how to adjust the mind during meditation. After meditation pay attention and do not indulge in random thinking. This is how to adjust the mind after meditation.

I have now described the three ways to adjust

the body, breath and mind. All three should be used simultaneously. I made three separate sections for discussion so that each could be presented clearly, but don't separate these procedures.

CHAPTER SIX

The Principle of Chih Kuan

During meditation arrange the torso and four limbs as well as possible, and adjust the breath. The mind is the most difficult to tame. The human mind always likes to chase after external things. Although you would like to recall your errant mind back to the body, this is a not an easy task to accomplish, so we must learn and practice the principles of Chih Kuan, which will allow us to meet this goal. After practicing the three adjustments, learn the principles of Chih Kuan. Even if you have never heard of the way of adjustment, you can still study the principles of Chih Kuan.

Chih means "rest". We have to stop our random thinking. Random thinking is like a monkey which knows no moment of stillness or peace. If this is so, what steps can we take to stop it? If we want the monkey to stop its activity, we have to tie it to a wooden stake, so that he can no longer jump at random. The first step towards practicing Chih is called Hsi Yuan Tzu (determination through tying up attractions). The mind's random activity must be occupied with a specific subject, either concept or object. This attractive subject is called Yuan (the attractive). The mind thinks randomly first of a, then of b, then of c and d. This is called Pan Yao (being hooked by the attractive). We tie our minds to some spot, as we might tie up a monkey, so that our mind will not be attracted by anything else, a process we call 'achieving rest by tying up the attractive'.

There are several ways to cure the mind's problems. I will illustrate two of these to choose from. The first method is to tie the mind to the tip of the nose — free of any random thoughts, focus the mind's eye on the tip of the nose to watch the breath. When you watch the entry and exit of the breath, you see neither where the breath comes from nor where it returns. After extensive practice, your random thoughts will gradually subside.

The second method is to tie the mind to the bottom of the abdomen: the center of gravity of our body is in the lower abdomen, so tying our minds to this place gives us perfect balance. When we do this, we should imagine a straight line from the nose and throat to the abdomen, entering and exiting through our nostrils. After prolonged practice, our mind's random thinking may diminish. This practice can also help in adjusting the breath.

When we have learned to rest by tying up the attractive, we can move on to Chih Hsin Chih "achieving rest by controlling the mind". What is Chih Hsin Chih? Hsi Yuan deals with the mind's subjectivity. Now Chih Hsin Chih can directly deal with the mind itself, allowing us to control and stop thought when we discern it in our mind, and prevent the possibilities of being hooked by the attractive. This training is far deeper and far more subtle than Hsi Yuan Chih.

As the next step, we learn T'í Chen Chih (resting by understanding the truth). This practice is on a level even higher than Chih Hsin Chih. The two methods just described are preparatory steps for learning to rest. When you practice this method you will acquire true rest.

What is T'í Chen Chih? T'í means "understanding"; Chen means "truth". When you try to discern your thoughts they suddenly disperse, become empty and random, and lose all value. If we don't try to perceive our thoughts, the mind remains in a state of void. If in addition all random thinking and conflict are not intentionally controlled, the mind may achieve a state of rest in a natural way. When you dispel empty, random thoughts the mind is close to truth. In this state the mind truly knows rest.

When you practice T'i Chen Chih during meditation, close the eyes, and reflect on the memory of your physical growth. We grow from infancy to childhood, maturity, old age, and death. Our cells constantly regenerate, without a moment's pause. There is no physical or mental state to which I can permanently hold and claim as my body. Again we reflect on the mind's thoughts. Thought after thought passes through our minds. The most recent of these is just past, the present thought continues, and the future thought is imminent. Which of these thoughts may I consider to be my true thought? From this we can see that as random mind perishes it is reborn, and all is empty and random. After much practice, we can stop this process of random thought naturally so that the mind remains in a state of truth.

As we learn meditation, our mind easily loses concentration in the beginning stages. This loss of concentration allows the mind to drift. The way to prevent the mind from losing concentration is to learn the technique of achieving rest. Repeated practice teaches our mind to remain in a state of rest. When rest is achieved, we easily become inattentive and drift into sleep. Curing this drowsiness requires visualization. Visualization doesn't mean looking outward, but rather closing the eyes and looking inward, to the mind.

There are three types of visualization. One is called visualizing the void. In this method, we try to visualize all things in the universe as constantly undergoing change, whether they be as large as mountains and rivers, or as small as our bodies and minds. Everything is impermanent. We must look into our minds and visualize this. This is called visualization of the void.

After long years of this practice, you can look into your mind during meditation and find that every thought in the mind has a subject, either an idea or an event. All things in the world result from the interactions of original conditions and ensuing events. For example, the seeds of various grains can sprout. This is an original condition. Water and soil can nourish these seeds. These are the ensuing events, the catalysts. If we store these seeds in a barn, and do not sow them, they would never sprout. Thus there is original condition lacking a catalyst. All things in the world are produced by the meeting of original conditions with a catalyst, and perish by their separation.

Our thoughts are chimerical. Do not try to hang on to them. If we visualize the attainment of goals, we are visualizing an illusion. Relatively speaking, visualization of the void belongs to the realm of non-being, and visualizing illusion belongs to the realm of being. Despite extensive study of visualization, we have not achieved perfection. We should therefore continue our study. When we visualize the void, we should be free from any prejudice that the vision must be void. If we visualize illusion, we create the illusory. Don't become attached to the concepts of void and illusion. Let your mind rely on nothing. If we achieve this, our minds become like hollow caves from which we can witness the external light. This is called visualizing the middle.

Superficially it appears that we are making distinctions in our discussion of this Tzu Kuan principle. In actual practice the practitioner can use his mind freely. Sometimes he may prefer to use resting, sometimes he may prefer to use visualization. Be determined in unifying your thoughts. This is called resting. Directing thoughts is called visualization. When we practice resting, we never abandon the use of visualization. When we practice visualization, we do not abandon the use of resting. Feel free to use both methods, and don't let yourself get confused by their apparent contradictions.

CHAPTER SEVEN

The Six Mystical Steps

In Chapter Four, we discussed adjustment. Though we tried to present the three adjustments of the breath, body, and mind equally, this introduction gave preferential treatment to the adjustment of the body. In Chapter Six, we discussed the principle of Chih Kuan, which is primarily a discussion of the mind. In this chapter, the six mystical steps, emphasis is on the breath.

Breath is the origin of life. Anyone who cannot breathe will soon die. The nervous system cannot sustain its reflexes and the mind dies. His life is finished. Breath alone makes it possible for us to connect the body and the mind, and maintain life. The entry and exit of air through our nostrils depends on this breath. Although it is usually invisible to our eyes, breath has both form and weight. Since it has both weight and form, during its passage it is also a material part of our body. We realize that entry and exit of the breath depend entirely on our mind, and that it is part of the spirit. Since breath can connect the body and the mind, we know breath itself is part of the body and the mind.

The six mystical steps will teach the practitioner to manage the technique of breathing. It is a method of continuous meditation. After learning the principles of Chih Kuan, the practitioner can go further to study the six mystical steps. Even without practicing the principles of Chih Kuan, he may begin the study of the six mystical steps.

Step One:
Counting practice and fulfillment

The six mystical steps are: counting, following, resting, visualization, returning, and clarifying. What is counting? Counting is to count breaths. Counting breaths has two levels. The first of these is to practice counting. After entering meditation, try to adjust the breath so it becomes perfectly smooth and peaceful, then count slowly from one to ten, placing the count on either the inhalation or the exhalation. When you focus on counting, do not lose concentration. If you lose concentration before ten is reached, begin the process over, starting at one. This is called counting practice.

The second level of counting breaths is called counting fulfillment. After much practice, you become gradually skillfull enough to count from one to ten without confusion. Your inhalations and exhalations become gentle and soft. When you reach this point, your breathing is so regular that you no longer need to count. This state is called the counting fulfillment.

Step Two:
Following practice and fulfillment

After this, we should give up the practice of counting, and proceed to study the following technique. This technique also has two levels, the first of which is called the following practice. We give up counting and let our mind follow the entry and exit of the breath. The mind accompanies the breath and the breath accompanies the mind, closely linked to each other, the breath becoming gentle and soft. This is called the following practice. The second level of this practice is called the following fulfillment. Once you master the following technique, the breath becomes very gentle, and it feels like you could breathe simply through your skin. The mind is placid and still. The attainment of this state is called the following fulfillment.

If, after a long period of practice, you feel that the breath is not yet gentle enough, give up the practice of following and begin the practice of resting.

Step Three:
Resting practice and fulfillment

Resting also has two levels. The first one is called the resting practice. The mind no longer follows the breath. Now gently focus your mind on the tip of the nose. This is called the resting practice. After a long period of practice, you will no longer feel that you have a mind or a physical body, and will enter into a state of deep meditation. This is called the resting fulfillment. Having reached this level of deep meditation, continue to visualize light in your mind until it becomes bright. Don't rest on your laurels, but begin the study of visualization.

Step Four:
Visualization practice and fulfillment

Visualization also has two levels. The first of these is the visualization practice. In meditation carefully visualize the breath entering and exiting the body, like a breeze in the air that lacks physical substance.

This is called the visualization practice. After a long period practicing visualization, you can mentally watch the breath entering and exiting through every pore in your body. This is called the visualization fulfillment. In the previous chapter, we discussed resting and visualization. These terms have a different meaning in this chapter. In

the previous chapter, we used resting and vis
ization, to focus on training the mind. In this cha
ter the focus is on training the breath. Aft
practicing visualization for some time, devote the
next period of study to the returning practice.

Step Five:
Returning practice and fulfillment

Returning, like the other techniques, has two
levels. The first of these is the returning practice.
Once you have used your mind to visualize the
breath, the mind acquires the skill of intelligent
visualization. This skill is distinct from intellectual
activity, but this opposition is relative, not
absolute. The practitioner lets his mind trace the
origin of his thoughts. This is called the returning
practice.

The second level of the returning practice is
called the returning fulfillment. This intelligent
visualization arises from the mind. Since it has
arisen within the mind, it should fall within the
mind, too. One rising, one falling. These are elu-
sive and unreal. The rising and falling of the mind
is like ripples on water. Ripples are not the water
itself. We have to wait until the surface of the water
is smooth before we can see the water itself. The
rising and falling of the mind is like a ripple, which
is not truly mind.

We should visualize our true mind, where

othing arises, then it is non-
...becomes the void. If it is the
...no visualizing mind. If there is
...the mind, then there is no state for
...and both state and intellectual activ-
...ear. This is called returning fulfillment.
...ou have reached the level of returning ful-
...ent, your mind retains only the concept of
...turning. Go on to the practice of clarification.

Step Six:
Clarification practice and fulfillment

Clarification has two levels also, the first called the clarification practice. When the mind is clarified, there will be no thoughts to distinguish. This is called the clarification practice. The second level is clarification fulfillment, in which the mind stays as still as still water, all random thinking expelled. You can then perceive your true mind. This doesn't mean there is both a true mind and a random-thinking mind. The mind returns from random thinking, and attains truth. This is like a ripple disappearing into the surface of water.

In the six mystical steps, counting and following comprise the preparatory work to use for deep meditation. Resting and visualization are for prolonged meditation. Returning and clarification are the fruit of this meditation. In these six mystical steps, resting should be regarded as the main training, with visualization simply an aid to the resting practice. Then the mind can be clearly disciplined, and you can receive the fruits of meditation, which are the returning and clarification.

CHAPTER EIGHT

Conclusion: The Relationship Between Theory and Practice

I n this work I gave a theoretical presentation of essential principles, and described the methods I practiced myself. My experiences are a testament to the methods' results. When theory and experience both unite, effects will naturally be produced. If you study a body of knowledge, or devote yourself to cultivation, you are making a big mistake if you only pursue theory, and don't pay attention to practice. No matter how profound your achievement in theoretical learning, if you do not go on practicing, all this theory is like building a house on the beach - the foundation is not stable.

As the saying goes, "Just talking about food will not make you full." If someone tells you which is the tastiest food, the most delicious, but you haven't eaten it yet, how can you become full? There is another type of person who is afraid that the theory might be too profound and too difficult to understand, so they cast aside the theory, and concentrate on practicing. However, practice without method is blind practice. Not only may you fail to benefit from the practice, but you may actually encounter serious pitfalls. This illustrates the problems of abandoning theory. The relationship between theory and practice should be like the wheel and axle of the cart, neither of which can move if the other is neglected.

Traditional Chinese meditation has recently attracted the world's attention, and its development has been rapid. There are many cases of chronic disease being healed through traditional Chinese meditation. The ancient and most popular art of acupuncture is once again being promoted. Though the arts of acupressure and massage may not enjoy as much fame as acupuncture, their theoretical application is nonetheless quite similar. Both serve as healing methods for disease. Of these, only meditation can serve as preventive medical care, which has been passed down through generations. Though it has been neglected for several centuries, the world is now paying attention, and this must be considered good news.

Meditation develops your innate energies. With practice, you can take charge of your mind and body, preventing disease before it arises. Shouldn't everyone make an effort to learn something like this? Superficially, meditation looks easy, but if you practice without patience, determination, and a long-term sense of devotion you will never realize its benefits. To give readers a guide to meditation, I have therefore summarized my many decades of experience. As for further explanation, this still awaits the study and research of future scholars of physiology and medicine. This study should help to further promote the role of traditional Chinese meditation in influencing and benefiting the whole world. This is my wish.

Finished in October, 1954.

ABOUT THE TRANSLATORS

Cheney Crow is a professor of linguistics at the University of Texas, Austin and has a Ph.D. in Foreign Language Educations, Applied Linguistics. She has a long history of meditation practice wich she origionally undertook to successfully manage pain. Her recent entry into the practice of T'ai Chi Ch'uan, under the guidance of Shi Fu Hwang, led to their collaboration on *Tranquil Sitting*.

Shi Fu Hwang was born in China in 1948 and completed college in Taiwan where he majored in Chinese History. For the last ten years he has devoted himself to the study and translation of Taoist and Buddhist texts. Shi Fu Hwang is a practitioner and teacher of several disciplines, including T'ai Chi Ch'uan and Toaist Yoga. He is a resident of Austin, Texas.

Index

Visualization prac-
tice 100

The Intrinsic Energies of T'ai Chi Ch'uan

Translated with commentary
by Stuart Alve Olson
8.5x5.5, $12.95, soft cover, 208 pages
ISBN 0-938045-13X

Stuart Alve Olson's landmark translation of T'ai Chi's most profound text--the Yang family's secret training journals on the nature and practical applications of intrinsic energy. Olson's commentary brilliantly explicates a work that will be an essential reference for any T'ai Chi practitioner.

"An excellent and extremely informative translation of an important body of work, that includes many principles and techniques not found in popular T'ai Chi manuals. Olson has written an accurate and lucid translation of a broad treatise, which, flavored by insights from his own experience of the oral teachings, renders an invaluable service in bridging the gap between theory and practice, enriching the understanding and practice of T'ai Chi players at all levels." Terry Dunn, author of *T'ai Chi For Health: The Yang Long Form.*

"This book is a very good document for both T'ai Chi players and instructors. Nowadays, no one has completely reached the high levels described here. Therefore this book really provides important goals to work towards attaining. If a dedicated T'ai Chi player can master these different "energies", they will help promote the art to a very high level." Master Jou, Tsung Hwa, author of *The Tao of T'ai Chi Ch'uan*

"I predict that this will be one of the most important works on T'ai Chi yet to be published in English. While the text itself is enlightening, the real pearls of knowledge contained in this book are to be found in Olson's commentary. Concepts and ideas typically mystified by practitioners are masterfully presented in a clear, direct manner." Dan Miller, editor of *Pa Kua Chang Journal*

The Jade Emperor's Mind Seal Classic

A Taoist Guide to Health,
Longevity and Immortality

Translated by Stuart Alve Olson,
$10.95, paper, 128 pages,
15 illustrations
ISBN 0-938045-10-5

The Taoists believe that there is no reason for a person to ever suffer physical illness. Death itself, whether from old age or sickness, is an unnecessary occurrence. Illness and death occur as a result of the dissipation of the Three Treasures - ching, ch'i and shen - our reproductive, life-sustaining and spiritual energies. The secret science of restoring, gathering and transforming these primal energies creates an elixir which will confer health, longevity and immorality.

The Jade Emperor's Mind Seal Classic, presented here in the first English translation is a primer on how to achieve these benefits. A supreme distillation of Taoist thought, the text works as the catalyst for a deep transformation of the being.

Stuart Olson, Taoist practitioner and long-time protege of Taoist and T'ai Chi Ch'uan master, T.T. Liang, provides a lucid translation of, and an insightful commentary on this key text. With its wealth of practical information the commentary will further reward the reader with deeper insight into other great Taoist works, such as the *Secret of the Golden Flower* and *Taoist Yoga: Alchemy and Immortality*.

Olson supplements this classic with a further translation of a rare treatise on *The Three Treasures of Immortality* taken from the Dragon Door sect of Taoism. A collection of aphorisms and quotes from various Taoist scriptures and masters, *The Three Treasures of Immortality*, sheds further light on the processes that will lead you to enhanced heath and longevity, if not enlightenment and immortality.

T'AI CHI CH'UAN

Imagination Becomes Reality

The Teachings of Master T. T. Liang

compiled by Stuart Alve Olson

Imagination Becomes Reality
The Teachings of Master T.T. Liang

Compiled by Staurt Alve Olson,
$21.95, paper, 292 pages,
7"x11", 600 illustrations
ISBN 0-938045-09-1

T.T. Liang is one of the most revered living masters of T'ai Chi Ch'uan. Now in his nineties, he has taught T'ai Chi for over fifty years. As a senior student to Cheng Man-ch'ing and as author of the best-selling *T'ai Chi Ch'uan for Health and Self-Defense* he helped introduce T'ai Chi to America.

This book presents the very heart of Liang's teachings, including his own version of the Yang style 150 posture solo form. Taken from T.T.'s own notes, this is the most comprehensive description of the form ever presented. Rare interviews and articles by T. T. Liang explore the basic principles and meaning of this increasingly popular martial art.

The remarkable photography both captures the full power, grace and subtlety of T'ai Chi while providing a detailed count by count presentation of each posture.

"Master T.T. Liang is a Chinese martial arts treasure in Western society. He was a true pioneer in the development of T'ai Chi Ch'uan in the United States of America."
    Dr. Yang Jwing-ming, author of Yang Style T'ai Chi Ch'uan

"This profound yet practical book...has much to offer practitioners of T'ai Chi and those intrigued by the concept of heightened awareness."
    Australian Bookseller and Publisher

Cultivating the Ch'i

Chen Kung Series, Volume One

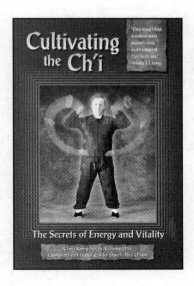

Translated by Stuart Alve Olson
$12.95, soft cover, 164 pages,
5-1/2" x 8-1/2",
101 illustrations,
ISBN 0-938045-11-3

Your foundation for health and self-defense, this is the first English translation of a work considered by the Chinese to be the Bible of T'ai Chi Ch'uan.

Taken from the training notes of T'ai Chi's most famous family, the Yangs, the book gives you detailed advice on breathing techniques, energy generation, meditation, ch'i-kung and much more.

You will appreciate the insightful commentary by Stuart Olson, based on his own extensive experience as a T'ai Chi instructor.

"Chen Kung's book is without question second to none on the subject of T'ai Chi Ch'uan."
— Master T.T. Liang

"If you are interested in physical immortality, practice yoga, meditate or would like to explore a very ancient, revered and effective way of maintaining physical vitality and youthfulness, you can learn a lot from this book that you would simply never find elsewhere."
— New Age Retailer

Order Form

Name _____ Phone _____

Address _____

City _____ State _____ ZIP _____

Country _____

Title	Price	Quantity	Total Price
Cultivating the Ch'i	$12.95	_____	_____
Imagination Becomes Reality	$21.95	_____	_____
Intrinsic Energies	$12.95	_____	_____
Jade Emperor	$10.95	_____	_____
Tranquil Sitting	$9.50	_____	_____

Subtotal _____

MN Residents add
6.5% Sales Tax _____

Shipping &
Handing ($3.00 for
first book, $1.00 for
each additional book.
Double S&H for
non-U.S. orders.) _____

Totals _____

❏ Check/Money Order Enclosed
❏ VISA ❏ Mastercard
❏ Amex ❏ Discover   Expires_____

Card #_____
Signature _____

Credit Card orders only: 1-800-247-6553
Dragon Door Publications
P.O. Box 4381, St. Paul, MN 55104 • ph. (612)645-0517

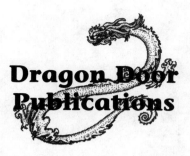

Dragon Door Publications

Dragon Door Publications also publishes a line of videos, audio tapes, and special reports and has a mail order catalog devoted to items on martial arts, meditation and Eastern philosophy. You may be especially interested in our three volume companion video to the book *Imagination Becomes Reality*.

Write, call or use our order form to receive a one year free subscription to our catalog.

Dragon Door Publications
P.O. Box 4381
St. Paul, MN 55104
(612) 645-0517
Fax (612) 644-5676